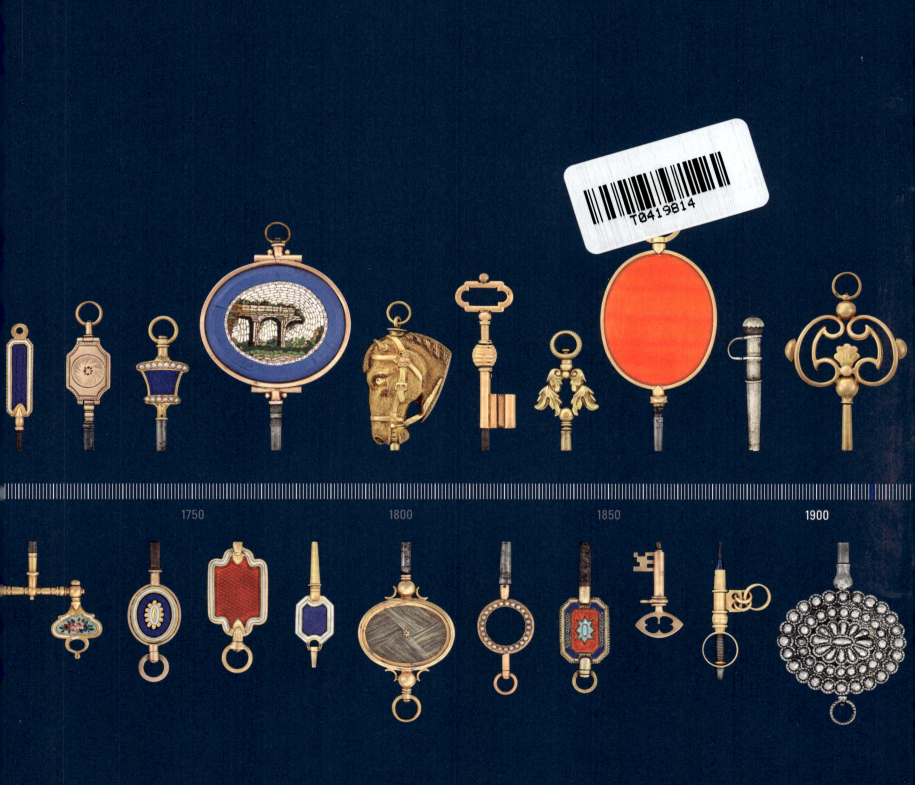

PATEK PHILIPPE MUSEUM

Treasures from The Antique Collection
The Emergence of the Watch

1500	1600	1700	1800	1900

Peter Friess

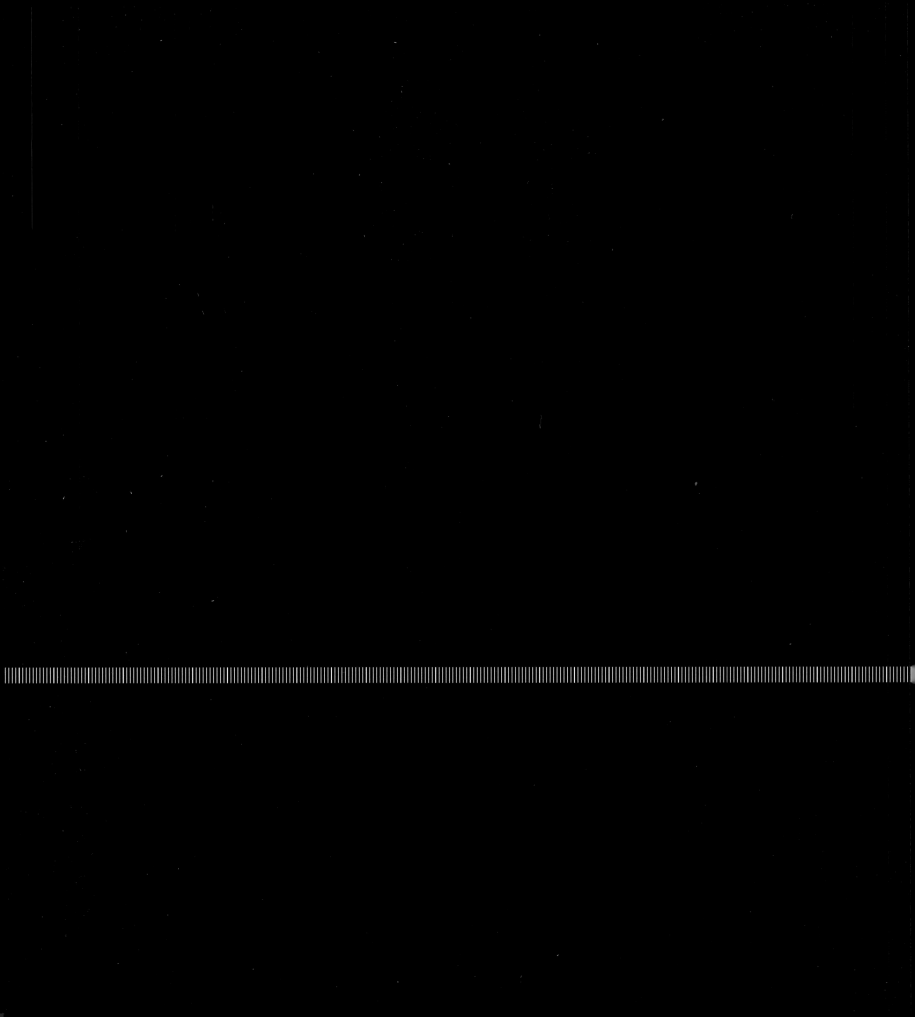

PATEK PHILIPPE MUSEUM

Treasures from The Antique Collection
The Emergence of the Watch

| 1500 | 1600 | 1700 | 1800 | 1900 |

2022

Author
Peter Friess, Director and Curator
Patek Philippe Museum

Concept and Design
Birgit Binner, tg2b

Scientific Editing
Arthur Molella

Photography
Photo Studio Fabien Cruchon
Graziano Villa, page 7

Image Retouching
Oeil Absolu Sàrl

Paper and Font
Finesse Premium Silk 170 g/sqm, UPM
Univers, Linotype

Published by teNeues Publishing Group
www.teneues.com

© 2022 Patek Philippe Museum
Any reproduction must be approved by
Patek Philippe SA

Patek Philippe Museum
Rue des Vieux-Grenadiers 7
CH-1205 Genève
www.patekmuseum.com
info@patekmuseum.com

Deutsche Nationalbibliothek
dnb.dnb.de

Library of Congress Control Number
2022935379

ISBN
978-3-96171-396-7

Preface by Philippe Stern	6
Honorary President, Patek Philippe SA	
Precision and Beauty	

The Revolution in Horology	8
after 1500	
Europe and the Advent of the Mechanical Watch	

The Invention of the Portable Timekeeper	10
1500–1600	
Clocks in Little Boxes	

Geneva Becomes a Watchmaking Center	14
1600–1700	
A Huguenot Legacy	

The Founding of Jean Toutin's Workshop	18
1600–1675	
Painting on Enamel	

Enamel Painting in Geneva	26
1630–1730	
The School of Huaud	

Science Revolutionizes Timekeeping	30
1575–1675	
Jost Bürgi and Christiaan Huygens	

Division of Labor and the "Fabrique genevoise"	34
1650–1750	
The Watch in an Age of Enlightenment	

Invention of the Marine Chronometer	38
1700–1825	
A Princely Sum of Prize Money	

The Art of Watchmaking Conquers the Far East	42
1730–1840	
Geneva's Supply Chain to China	

Paired Watches for the Chinese Market	50
1770–1840	
In Pursuit of Symmetry: Yin and Yang	

Watches for the Ottoman Empire	54
1750–1850	
Reckoning with the Moon	

Breathing Life into Machines	58
1730–1860	
The Magic World of Automata	

Pioneers of Modern Watchmaking	66
1750–1850	
Abraham-Louis Breguet's Horological Genius	

Self-Winding Watches	70
1775–1810	
A Historical Mystery	

Watches Adapt to the Modern World	74
1790–1825	
Changing Times	

Ornamental Watches for Women	80
1780–1890	
Form Watches as Fashion Statements	

Time Made Audible	84
1700–1820	
From Striking to Music Players	

Measuring the Smallest Time Units	88
1780–1830	
Tenths, Hundredths, and Thousandths of a Second	

High-Precision Watches	92
1750–1850	
Shrinking the Chronometer	

Eclecticism and Historicism	96
1815–1860	
Old versus New versus Old	

Crowning of the Pocket Watch	100
1750–1850	
Revolution in Winding and Setting Watches	

Preface by Philippe Stern

Precision and Beauty

This volume together with its companion volume provides new images and information on priceless treasures from the collections of the Patek Philippe Museum. Included are the company's own watches dating back to 1839, "The Patek Philippe Collection," which formed the core of the collection I started in the 1960s, and "The Antique Collection" with historic items that go back to the dawn of the portable timekeeper around 1500. Combined they represent a unique homage to Europe's horological heritage, for which I have long felt a passionate affinity. These books are intended for anyone, from generalists to experts, who is drawn to historic machines of unparalleled precision and beauty.

Each book might be compared to a play in twenty acts in chronological and thematic sequence. Each act is introduced by a concise historical account setting the scene. The stars of our drama are timepieces that have made history. All have been carefully auditioned (indeed chiming sonneries sing to you) by our expert curatorial team for their precision performance, dramatic presence, and beauty—a special beauty that not only resides on an enamel painted surface, but grows directly from choreographed motions of wheels and springs hidden within. These watches are masterpieces of form and function. Therefore, unlike most books of this type, we emphasize their inner mechanisms.

Representative artifacts document a confluence of aesthetics and technical genius in the mechanical watch. This complex history involves a constant dialog between innovation and tradition, which I regard as an essential tension. Nothing speaks more eloquently to this tension than the Calibre 89, introduced by Patek Philippe in 1989 in commemoration of the company's 150th anniversary. With its unprecedented 33 complications and revolutionary technologies, it is the superstar of the latter acts of our drama. But it also converses with the past, defying time itself and evoking time-honored traditions of the master watchmakers of the Vallée de Joux. Calibre 89 represented a major turning point in watchmaking that secured the success of the luxury mechanical watch in the face of ubiquitous, highly accurate, and inexpensive quartz watches, which ironically Patek Philippe had a hand in inventing.

Our books are dedicated to the creative spirits who have worked at our company over the past 183 years to realize the visions of our founders, Messieurs Patek and Philippe, to build the most precise and beautiful watches in the world.

Philippe Stern
Honorary President, Patek Philippe SA

"If you want to know the future,
you have only to reach into the past."

Philippe Stern in the Patek Philippe Archives, holding the Star Caliber 2000. Behind him are volumes documenting every watch produced by the company from 1839 onwards.

The watch shown on the left is the Calibre 89, which was in its day the most complicated watch ever built.

Patek, Philippe S.A.
Geneva, 1989
Caliber 32''', Prototype
Ø 88 mm; P-1989

The Revolution in Horology

1500   1600   1700   1800   1900

Europe and the Advent of the Mechanical Watch

As of the turn of the 16th century, European clocks began to get smaller. From tower clocks still seen in cities today, they evolved into table clocks, to pocket watches, and finally, around 1900, to wristwatches, the ultimate in personal time. Miniaturization represented a watershed in the history of the mechanical clock, commencing in the late 1200s. The emergence of the precision watch was part of the great European revolutions in technology and science. These revolutions begot the revolution in horology: Before 1500, clockmaking methods were mostly empirical; after 1500, they became creative, scientific, modern.

The use of springs rather than weights to power mechanical clocks was the critical breakthrough. It broke the size barrier, leading the way to watches. It also unleashed a cascade of creativity and inventions like the fusee, which made the clock more precise by adjusting for the variable force of the spring as it slowly unwinds. Geniuses like Leonardo da Vinci pondered such devices, and, soon after, principles and research emanating from Europe's Scientific Revolution were applied to clocks and watches. Eventually the Dutch mathematician and astronomer Christiaan Huygens combined pendulum and clock, overnight turning clocks into scientific instruments accurate to less than a minute per day. In watches, he devised an improved time regulator, a balance with hairspring still in use today.

The clock is one of the most complex and innovative mechanisms ever built. Why it was born in Europe is no great mystery. Scientific and technological progress required exact timekeepers, and all the necessary technical and craft skills were already in place. European patent laws nurtured horological innovation. The nascent watch industry initially depended on the patronage of royals, who took pride in the scientific knowledge and luxury represented in watches they owned. Eventually, watchmaking freed itself from dependency on its aristocratic clients.

Renowned for its luxury industries and its modern division-of-labor system called "La Fabrique genevoise," Geneva emerged as the epicenter of watchmaking. The city's watchmakers understood the dual appeal of science and aesthetics. Drawing on local metalworking and enamel-painting skills, they created some of the most beautiful and accurate watches ever made. Timekeepers produced in this small Swiss city soon dominated world markets.

Peter Friess
Director and Curator, Patek Philippe Museum

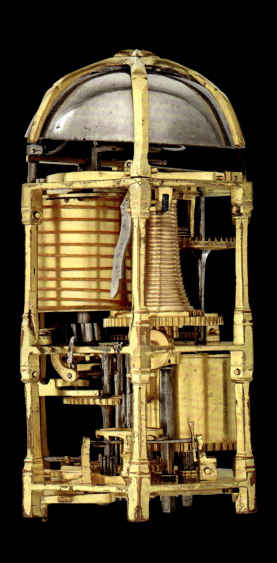

Back to the Future

This hexagonal table clock is made in gilded bronze. It is fitted with a striking mechanism and an alarm. Its dial indicates the hours (XII) and the alarm (12). The fusee equalizes the varying power of the mainspring, a mechanical principle which was discovered in 1450 and applied to watches for 500 years.

Attributed to Pierre de Fobis
Aix-en-Provence, circa 1540
H. 162 mm; S-566

The cardinal virtue of Temperance, represented as a young woman, intervenes on the mechanism of a wall clock to regulate it.

Fondation Martin Bodmer,
Cod. Bodmer 49, fol. 11r

The Invention of the Portable Timekeeper

1500　　　　　1600　　　　　1700　　　　　1800　　　　　1900

Clocks in Little Boxes

The first mechanical timekeepers appeared in 13th-century Europe in response to the needs of monasteries to summon the fraternity to prayer. Mechanical clocks were already more reliable than sundials and water clocks. The clockwork was impressively large, and the technology was very simple: the gradual descent of a weight, suspended from a rope coiled around a horizontal axis, rotated the wheels of the clockwork.

The mid-15th-century idea of replacing the weight with a spring opened the way to portable timekeepers. The first spring-powered timepieces were table clocks, which gradually spread throughout Europe. French versions often took the form of small, hexagonal towers. They chimed the hours and the quarters, and some had alarms (page 13, S-197).

Wearable timepieces probably originated shortly after 1500 in Nuremberg, Germany, a major producer of scientific instruments. Nuremberg, with Augsburg, also attracted leading goldsmiths and watchmakers. The best evidence for the watch's origins points to Nuremberg locksmith and clockmaker Peter Henlein (1485–1542), described in 1511 as "very nearly the first of those who discovered how to put small clocks into little boxes." He was reportedly paid fifteen florins for a small, spherical watch in 1524, the earliest known date of watch manufacture.

The first portable German timepieces, also called "Dosenuhren," consisted of small clockworks installed in cylindrical cases topped by horizontal dials. But early watches were notoriously unreliable and needed to be reset—sometimes using a sundial added to the housing—and rewound two or three times each day (page 12, S-885).

Miniaturization progressed throughout the Renaissance, especially in Italy and France, transforming timepieces into personal accessories that were often worn around the neck. Deserving special mention are the spherical watches designed in about 1550 by Jacques de La Garde, watchmaker to King Henry II of France (1519–1559).

Adjusted with the Sun

A sundial, which was used to reset the time on a mechanical timekeeper until the 20th century, is visible along with a compass on the hinged cover of the case, to orient the gnomon of the sundial to the right relationship with the sun. An alternative to the fusee in compensating for the decreasing power of the slackening mainspring was the stackfreed. It is a spring-loaded cam mechanism which evens out the mainspring's force.

Attributed to Hans Koch and Markus Purman
Germany, 1570
Ø 71 mm; S-584

The Invention of the Portable Timekeeper

1500 **1600** 1700 1800 1900

Travel Alarm

This table clock with alarm has its original leather case, evidence that these timepieces were meant to accompany travelers. It is made up of two parts and is fitted with an alarm system. During the day, the bottom part with the dial was typically used for telling the time. When needed, the top piece with the alarm mechanism could be connected to ring the silver-colored bell.

This clock movement is made almost entirely of iron. Until 1550, clocks and watches were made by locksmiths, who were accustomed to working in iron.

Germany, circa 1550
Ø 46 mm (clock); S-885

Miniature Clock Tower

Table clocks shaped like miniature towers are the earliest surviving timepieces equipped with gears. This late Gothic example indicates the hours and has an alarm that sounds when the bell under the dome is struck. The movement is powered by a mainspring rather than a weight. A mainspring's power is, unfortunately, not constant, but weakens as it unwinds, affecting the accuracy of the clock. In a manuscript from 1490, Leonardo da Vinci (1452–1519) gives a detailed explanation of the conical fusee mechanism (shown here behind the dial), which ingeniously compensates for this irregularity.

Nicolas Morel
Paris, circa 1530
H. 109 mm; S-197

Geneva Becomes a Watchmaking Center

A Huguenot Legacy

In 1601, Geneva's watchmakers drafted their own "Orders and Rules" for their craft. Unlike other European watchmakers, they had been associated with goldsmiths' rather than locksmiths' guilds before splitting into separate organizations of master craftsmen. The introduction in 1560 of the Sumptuary Laws prohibiting the wearing of jewelry, influenced by the reformer John Calvin (1509–1564), had compelled many Geneva goldsmiths to turn to a new trade, namely watchmaking. It is doubtless for this reason that Geneva's watchmakers excelled in the production of richly decorated gilded watches (page 16, S-270).

But other unique social factors came into play in Geneva's rise as a center for the luxury watch industry. Among the most important was the city's reputation for tolerance at a time of political and religious strife throughout the rest of Europe. Around 1540, French Protestants began to flee for safe haven in Geneva. Oppressed in France by the 1551 Edict of Châteaubriant and persecuted after the Saint Barthélemy massacre in 1572, they came in great numbers during the 16th century, eventually making up a third of Geneva's population.

Known as Huguenots, they brought innovative methods and techniques to their adopted home. Among the most important of these were enamel painting and creating watches with such complications as the moon phases and other calendar indications. The Edict of Nantes—a law of tolerance—issued in 1598 afforded French Protestants temporary relief. But the law's revocation in 1685 refueled the exodus to Geneva, making the Calvinist stronghold the world capital of watchmaking (page 16, S-942).

But the Geneva market was not able to absorb all of its own prolific production. Other outlets were urgently needed, and the local craftsmen began to export their timepieces to the Ottoman Empire and Persia, carefully adapting them to the taste of their new clientele. A small colony of watchmakers even settled in Constantinople: Isaac Rousseau (1672–1747), father of the philosopher Jean-Jacques Rousseau (1712–1778), was among those who set out to conquer the Ottoman market.

Ice from the Gods

350 %

Rock crystal was frequently used in watch cases made between 1630 and 1675. Magic powers had long been attributed to rock crystals. In antiquity, this semi-precious stone was believed to be ice from the gods, which the sun could never melt.

Attributed to Jacques Sermand
Geneva, circa 1635
W. 24 mm; S-276

Geneva Becomes a Watchmaking Center

Cross Time

Watches in the shape of Latin crosses were intended to recall the Crucifixion of Christ. Like watches in the shape of human skulls, known as "memento mori," they referred more generally to the vanity of all humans in the face of death.

France, circa 1630
W. 34 mm; S-270

The case of this pendant watch is made of gold and has four covers. Each is decorated in white champlevé enamel and set with garnets. Inside the main cover, behind an oval garnet, is the portrait of an unknown man.

Jean-Henry Ester
Geneva, circa 1630
W. 29 mm; S-277

Man Behind Glass

Moon Face

In 17th-century Geneva, a timepiece with astronomical complications was called a "montre à mouvement de lune" (watch with lunar calendar). These rare watches were usually built with simple movements—those without any other horological complications—but this piece is fitted with an hour-striking and alarm mechanism. The additional complications made this watch one of the most complicated ever produced in Geneva during the 17th century.

Jean Rousseau II
Geneva, circa 1660
Ø 60 mm; S-942

Bouquet of Time

This bassine-cased watch is made of scroll-sawed gold and encrusted enamel ("en ronde-bosse"). The enamel painting on the dial represents a vase with polychrome flowers.

Jacques Cartier
Geneva, circa 1670
Ø 46 mm; S-228

In the last half of the 17th century, Geneva's watchmakers were partial to watches shaped like animals. Popular figures included dolphins, lions, dogs, doves, rabbits, ducks, and eagles.

Jean-Henry Ester
Geneva, circa 1660
W. 26 mm; S-248

Red-Eyed Dolphin

The Founding of Jean Toutin's Workshop

Painting on Enamel

Painting on enamel flourished at Blois in France around 1630 and reached Geneva at about the same time. French kings in this era frequently chose to reside in the Loire region, where their presence attracted numerous artisans who specialized in diverse arts and crafts, including watchmaking. Creative exchange ensued between the artistic crafts and horology, so that enamel paintings soon adorned the watch cases, transforming them into artworks.

The technique of painting on enamel was developed in the workshop of the goldsmith Jean Toutin (1578–1644), who was the first to apply metal oxide pigments and lavender oil to surfaces prepared with a base coat of white enamel. The process demanded the utmost skill, since decorated artifacts had to be fired step-wise many times in order to fuse color to substrate. The advantage of enameling was that the colors remained permanent. This was not the case with paintings in oil, gouache, or watercolor, which changed over time (page 19, S-1063).

Toutin is also credited with inventing the white enamel dial. Previously, dials were typically crafted in silver, brass, or gold and engraved with numerals. The first timepieces with dials of white enamel and black numerals appeared in Blois in France around 1640 and were rapidly adopted across Europe.

Toutin had many apprentices, including two of his sons, Henri (born 1614) and Jean II (born 1619), who followed in their father's footsteps. It is said that many Genevan craftsmen traveled to Blois to learn the new technique.

Watch cases with enamel dials became prestige items that every European aristocrat seemed to covet. The technique spread rapidly, reaching high levels in other parts of Europe—for instance, in Augsburg with its flourishing watchmaking industry, but also in Italy and Spain (page 24, S-466).

Field of Battle

This watch was most likely enameled by the inventor of the enamel painting technique, Jean Toutin (1578–1644). The battle scene was made after an engraving by the Italian artist Antonio Tempesta (1555–1630). It is an illustration from the "Metamorphoses" by the Latin poet Ovid.

Jean Toutin (enamel painter)
Blois, circa 1630
Josias Jolly (watchmaker)
Paris, circa 1630
Ø 44 mm; S-1063

The goldsmith Jean Toutin (1578–1644), inventor of the technique of enamel painting, is shown firing a painting in his workshop's high-temperature furnace. An apprentice stands behind him. Hanging from the ceiling is an enamel design for a watch case. The illustration is from a book Toutin published in 1619.

The Founding of Jean Toutin's Workshop

Love Scene

The scene on the dial shows the romance of Theagenes and Chariclea from Heliodorus of Emesa's "Aethiopica," a novel from the third century CE.

Henri and Jean Toutin (enamel painters)
Blois, circa 1645
Grégoire Gamot (movement)
Paris, circa 1645
Ø 51 mm; S-1045

Peak Artistry

Combining the work of watchmaker, goldsmith, jeweler, and enameler, this pendant watch is a triumph of craftsmanship. The thin gold case is entirely covered in blue enamel. The outer layer of gold is chased in high relief and then enameled in the technique called "émaillage sur ronde-bosse d'or." The feminine figures are taken from Abraham Bosse's (1604–1676) series of engravings entitled "The Cardinal Virtues."

Jehan Cremsdorff
Paris, circa 1650
Ø 59 mm; S-1054

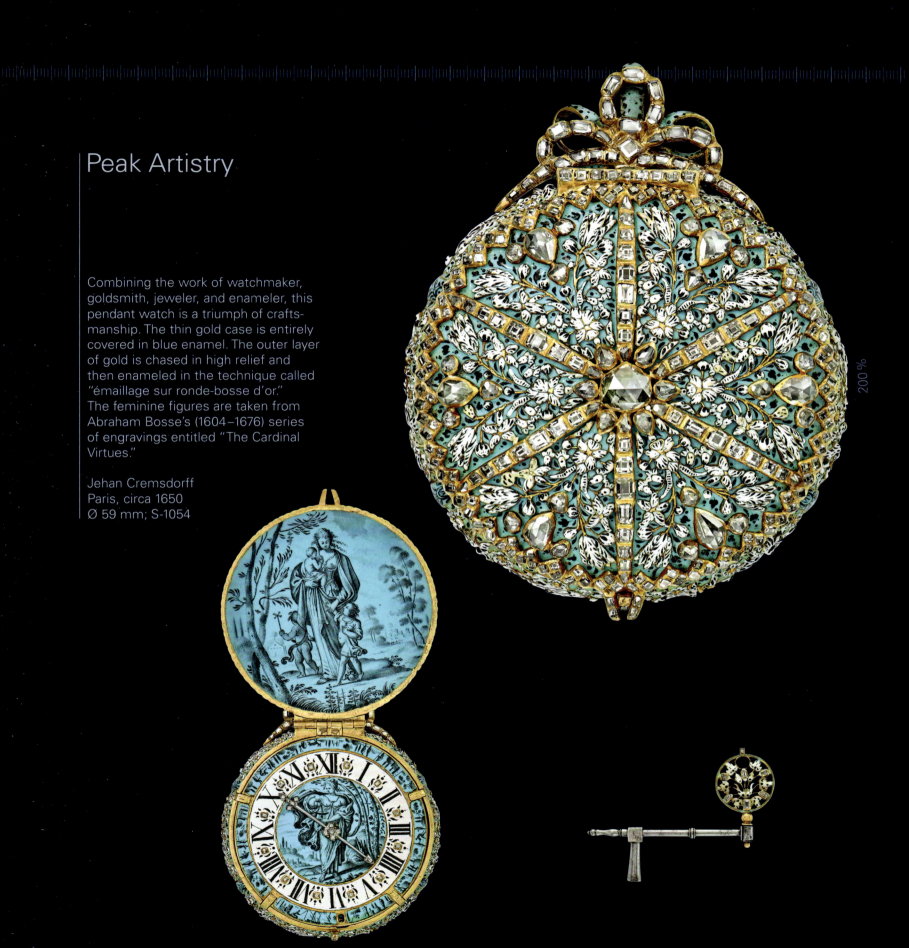

The Founding of Jean Toutin's Workshop

Cain and Abel

Biblical themes were common in early enamel-painted watches. The enamel painting on this watch's dial appears to tell the story of Cain and Abel, sons of Adam and Eve. The two brothers are depicted in a wood crossed by a river. Abel hides behind a bush while Cain aims his javelin at him, although the Bible does not specify how Cain killed his brother.

The case band of this pocket watch unscrolls with Biblical tales, including Jonah and the Whale, Samson slaying the Lion, and Belam with his donkey.

Jehan Augier
Paris, circa 1640
Ø 66 mm; S-1062

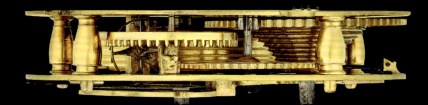

Illumination

The dial of this pendant watch bears one of the first enameled paintings ever made. This style is reminiscent of manuscript illuminations, which suggests a line of influence on the enamel painting of watches.

Josias Jolly (watchmaker)
Paris, circa 1635
Ø 53 mm; S-1066

The Founding of Jean Toutin's Workshop

Shape of the Heart

A fine example of craftsmanship from Augsburg, Germany, this heart-shaped pendant watch depicts Mary with the Infant Jesus alongside her sister Elizabeth and her son, John the Baptist. This image is based on a work of the Italian Renaissance artist Giulio Romano (1499–1546).

Johann Martin
Augsburg, circa 1675
W. 33 mm; S-360

The Sickle

The harbor of Messina in Italy, named "the Sickle" because of its shape, is shown on the lid of this watch: This illustration was made after a missing painting by the French artist Louis de Boullogne (1609–1674). The map is so precise and realistic that streets, houses, monuments, and the cathedral are clearly recognizable.

Giuseppe Bruno (enamel painter)
Messina, Italy, circa 1670
Ø 46 mm; S-466

Tulip Mania

Combined with the enamel painting, 341 rubies and 85 diamonds make this pocket watch one of the finest of its time. Bursting forth from the dial is a luxuriant basket of flowers: sweetheart roses, primroses, daffodils, carnations, pansies, tulips, and the famous Semper Augustus, whose bulbs could cost as much as a stately home in Amsterdam. On the inside cover is an enameled bouquet that also includes a Semper Augustus. The black background heightens the color of the flowers. Floral images were a recurrent motif in Dutch still-life painting.

Nicolas Bernard
Paris, circa 1645
Ø 58 mm; S-1082

The School of Huaud

Many Huguenot artisans fleeing France settled in Geneva. The city's thriving watchmaking trade gave them sufficient work, as enameling skills were in great demand. A typically French technique rapidly became a Genevan specialty.

Pierre Huaud I (1612–1680), who fled his native France at the age of eighteen, is believed to have introduced enamel watch painting in Geneva. He favored the so-called pointillé technique, in which miniscule dots of colored enamel are superimposed to create subtle transitions from one hue to another. There are no known paintings signed by Pierre Huaud I, but several watch cases can be attributed to him based on stylistic criteria.

The most talented of his sons was Pierre Huaud II (1647–1698), who specialized in mythological and historical scenes. Later in life he moved to Berlin, where he remained. His brothers Jean-Pierre Huaud (1655–1723) and Ami Huaud (1657–1724), also trained as miniaturists, entered into partnership. Summoned by the Prince-Elector of Brandenburg, the later Frederick I of Prussia (1657–1713), they, too, practiced their art in the Prussian capital. Around 1700, Jean-Pierre Huaud and Ami Huaud

With their distinctive style, the Huauds may be considered the founders of the Geneva school of enamel painting. The extraordinary quality of their work made this art form popular throughout Europe. Other enamel painters, such as Jean André I (1646–1714), Jean Mussard V (1681–1754), and Germain Colladon (1698–1747), perpetuated a tradition they had learned from illustrious predecessors. Colorful and exquisite miniatures by these talented enamelers contributed decisively to the success of Genevan watchmaking.

Meanwhile, the way timepieces were worn on the body changed. After more than a century in fashion, the pendant watch worn around the neck was abandoned in favor of a pocket watch or one housed in a protective case worn at the waist.

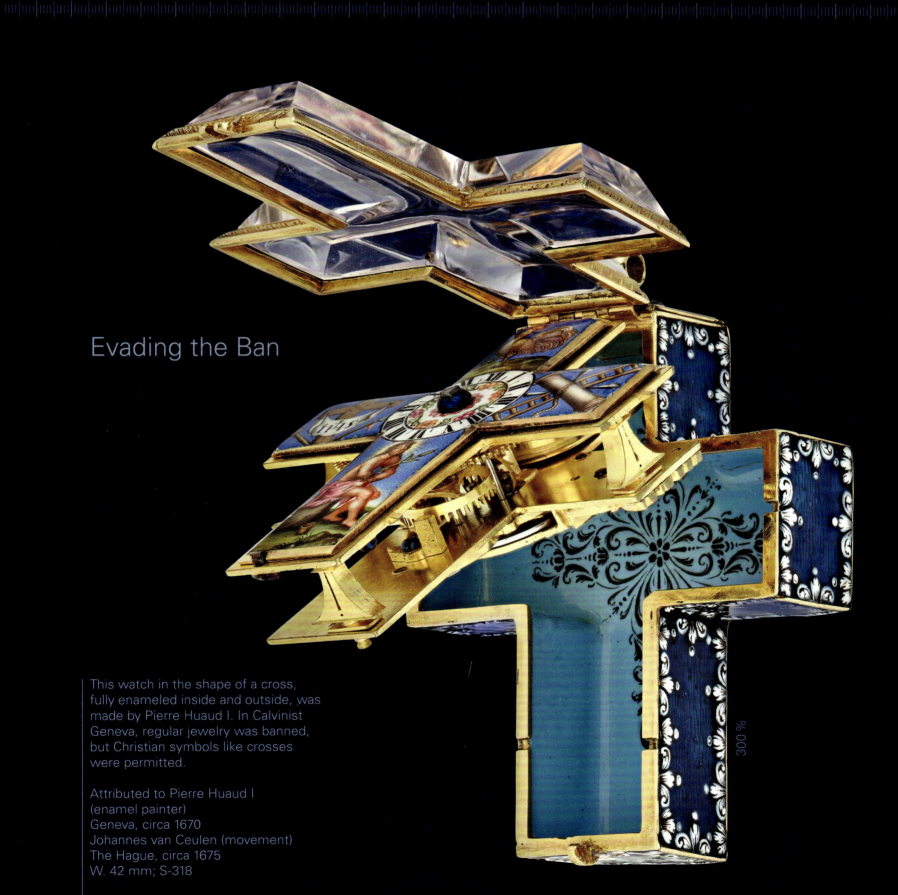

Evading the Ban

This watch in the shape of a cross, fully enameled inside and outside, was made by Pierre Huaud I. In Calvinist Geneva, regular jewelry was banned, but Christian symbols like crosses were permitted.

Attributed to Pierre Huaud I
(enamel painter)
Geneva, circa 1670
Johannes van Ceulen (movement)
The Hague, circa 1675
W. 42 mm; S-318

Enamel Painting in Geneva

Inspired by Titian

Family Tradition

Titian's "Venus and Adonis" from 1554 served as a model for this watch case, attributed to Pierre Huaud I (1612–1680). The young Adonis pulls back from Venus, resisting her desperate attempts to keep him by her side.

Attributed to Pierre Huaud I
(enamel painter)
Abraham Caillate (movement)
Geneva, circa 1670
Ø 36 mm; S-405

Titian, "Venus and Adonis," 1554,
Prado Museum, Madrid

Upon the death of Pierre Huaud I in 1680, his eldest son Jean-Pierre, who with his brothers inherited the family business, initially signed his cases painted in enamel: "Huaud le puis né fecit" (painted by the next-born Huaud [son]).

The Workshop of Jean-Pierre and Ami Huaud (enamel painters)
Berlin, circa 1690
Isaac Hasius (movement)
Haarlem, circa 1700
Ø 39 mm; S-260

Splendors of Spring

Anne of Austria

The trefoil shape of this case reinforces the watch's theme of nature in springtime. Pictured on the dial are two cherubs holding some garlands of delicate pink flowers.

Attributed to Pierre Huaud I
(enamel painter)
Geneva, circa 1665
Mathieu Gosselin (movement)
Rennes, circa 1665
W. 40 mm; S-945

This enamel portrait of Anne of Austria (1601–1666), Queen of France, was made after an engraving by the French artist Pierre Mignard (1612–1695). As wife of King Louis XIII (1601–1643), she is shown wearing her crown.

Pierre-Didier Lagisse
Geneva, circa 1660
Ø 32 mm; S-1014

Science Revolutionizes Timekeeping

Jost Bürgi and Christiaan Huygens

Precision clockmaking did not evolve from craft to science all at once. The Swiss clockmaker and scientific instrument maker Jost Bürgi (1552–1632) was a transition figure who mediated between clockmakers and scientists. He worked closely with the great astronomer Johannes Kepler (1571–1630). Before pendulum clocks became the scientific standard, Bürgi pushed horological precision to incredible heights with ingenious clocks that were accurate enough even to indicate seconds. His clocks, however, could not be reduced to the size of a watch.

Until 1657, the beauty of early timepieces easily surpassed their accuracy. They were primarily status objects. This changed abruptly when in 1673 the Dutch astronomer and mathematician Christiaan Huygens (1629–1695) published his epochal treatise, "Horologium Oscillatorium." Based on an observation by Galileo Galilei (1564–1642), Huygens explained the phenomenon of swinging pendulums, and he proposed that they could be used for time regulation in clocks.

The new clocks regulated by a pendulum deviated from perfection by less than one minute per day. Their accuracy is due to a natural law which states that the time of oscillation depends only on the length of the pendulum. Applying this principle to clocks was a true revolution in measuring time (page 32, S-474).

Huygens also invented an oscillating system for watches. He combined the balance with a spiral-shaped hairspring, so that the period of oscillation depended only on the mass of the balance and the elasticity of the hairspring. His invention transformed the watch into a precision instrument. In 1675 Huygens commissioned French watchmaker Isaac Thuret (1630–1706) to make a pocket watch with a balance and hairspring. At nearly the same time, the English scientist Robert Hooke (1635–1703) developed a similar oscillating system with a blade spring. His countryman Thomas Tompion (1639–1713) was among the first to apply on a large scale Huygen's notion of combining balances and hairsprings in watches (page 33, S-701).

The oscillation laws and the invention of both regulators—the pendulum and the balance with hairspring—instantly conquered the world of horology. Hands for minutes and seconds now joined the hour hand on dials of large and small timekeepers.

These timekeepers enabled researchers to observe natural phenomena with the greatest accuracy. Henceforth, watchmaking and science were bound to each other. Precise clocks ed to more scientific knowledge, which in turn led to still more accurate clocks—an interaction that continues today.

Supreme Accuracy

Jost Bürgi reduced the friction of the gears to a minimum. This clock has only one wheel, an oversized escapement wheel, driven by two small weights. The so-called cross-beat escapement moves very slowly, with an oscillation period of 12 seconds.

Attributed to Jost Bürgi
Prague, circa 1610
H. 555 mm; S-1100

Jost Bürgi by Anton Eisenhoit from the title page of Benjamin Bramer's report, Marburg, 1648 and 1684

Science Revolutionizes Timekeeping

Spiral Hairspring

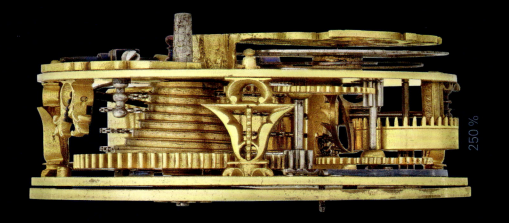

This watch embodied the most advanced technology of its day: it had the Huygens hairspring shaped like a spiral, still used today. It made the watch precise enough for indicating minutes. The minute hand was a new feature, to which the watchmaker added an artistic touch: it changed length as it followed the oval dial.

Henry Jones
London, circa 1675
Ø 60 mm; S-474

Sunrise to Sunset

Blade Hairspring

250 %

Hours are indicated in an aperture in the upper half of the dial. The sun symbol, which moves from sunrise to sunset, points to the hours in Roman numerals. After sunset, the sun transforms into a moon symbol. The Huygens spiral-shaped hairspring makes the watch precise enough to show not only the minutes, indicated by the long central hand, but even the seconds in the subdial.

Jean Deonna
Geneva, circa 1700
Ø 56 mm; S-826

This movement is fitted with an escapement with a straight blade spring, after the invention of Robert Hooke (1635–1703), the British physicist whose name is associated with the law of elasticity. At about the same time as Christiaan Huygens (1629–1695), Robert Hooke also developed an oscillating system for watch balances, in connection with his own invention of a straight blade spring—a solution that did not survive.

Movement after Robert Hooke
London, England, circa 1675
Ø 41 mm; S-701

The Watch in an Age of Enlightenment

A European intellectual and philosophical movement of the late 17th and 18th centuries, the Enlightenment stood for science and invention. The period was also known as the Age of Reason.

The "Encyclopédie," or, more formally, the "Encyclopedia, or a Systematic Dictionary of the Sciences, Arts and Crafts," was the signature publication of the French Enlightenment. Published between 1751 and 1772, it was co-edited by Denis Diderot (1713–1784) and Jean le Rond d'Alembert (1717–1783). It comprised 35 volumes, with more than 72,000 articles, and was especially famous for its magnificent plates illustrating tools and crafts. Among the authors were philosophers like Voltaire (1694–1778), who established a watchmaking workshop on the outskirts of Geneva (page 36, S-694). In total, more than 140 people contributed to this vast editorial project.

The new intellectual energy spread through the urban centers of Europe, influencing nearly every aspect of daily life. In Paris, the "Académie royale des sciences" was founded in 1666 to promote the sciences, including horological research. Timekeepers were increasingly used as scientific instruments.

While surveying advances in science and technology, a large section of the encyclopedia was devoted to the latest arts and crafts. One of the most technically capable writers in the "Encyclopédie" was the watchmaker Ferdinand Berthoud (1727–1807). Making his career in France, in 1770 he was appointed "Watchmaker-mechanic to the King and to the Navy." He was also elected to the Royal Society of London in 1764.

In Geneva, the division-of-labor system significantly raised productivity: It is estimated that between 1700 and 1789 watch production increased tenfold. Specialized craftsmen produced components for watches, which other watchmakers would afterwards assemble in their workshops. More than sixty distinct crafts were involved. Specialists included goldsmiths, lapidaries, and enamelers, all of whom worked collaboratively in an organization called the "Fabrique genevoise" (page 37, S-411).

Beauty Comes from Within

The back plate of this pocket watch is set with diamonds and skeletonized, making the inner workings completely visible through the glass cover. The movement itself is transformed into a heart-shaped piece of jewelry, complementing the diamonds on the outside of the case. Inner and outer beauty thus combine in a singular way.

Louis de La Corbière & Cie
Geneva, circa 1770
Ø 29 mm; S-847

Division of Labor and the "Fabrique genevoise"

The enamel painting is a portrait of François-Marie Arouet, known as Voltaire (1694–1778), at age eighty-one. It is not commonly known that in 1770 this famed French Enlightenment figure opened a watchmaking business, the "Manufacture royale," in the village of Ferney, near Geneva.

The dial is signed by two Geneva watchmakers, Pierre Dufour and Louis Céret, who co-managed Voltaire's enterprise.

Dufour & Céret
Ferney, circa 1775
Ø 40 mm; S-694

Voltaire, Watchmaker

Fabrique genevoise

A product of the "Fabrique genevoise," this pocket watch is made of gold and ornamented with champlevé enamel, paillons, and pearls. The subject of the enamel painting is an Allegory of Fertility, after a work by the prominent French portrait painter Louise-Elisabeth Vigée-Le Brun (1755–1842).

Antoine des Roches
Geneva, circa 1795
Ø 53 mm; S-283

Fashionable during the first half of the 18th century, châtelaines consist of a belt hook or clip (a folded blade straddling the belt), a set of ornamental plates followed by suspension chains and charms. Both the back cover of the watch and the châtelaine feature the Greek fictional characters Daphnis and Chloe, abandoned children who herded flocks for their foster parents.

Attributed to Jean-Louis Richter (enamel painter)
Philippe Terrot (movement)
Geneva, circa 1795
Ø 53 mm; S-411

High Fashion

Catullus and Lesbia

On the watch's back cover is a portrait of the poet Catullus (c. 84–c. 54 BC) and his muse Lesbia, after a painting by Angelica Kauffmann (1741–1807). Framing the central image are busts of the French philosopher and writer Jean-Jacques Rousseau (1712–1778), at left, and Voltaire (1694–1778). The case is made of engine-turned gold, flinqué, champlevé, and spangled enamel.

Bordier Frères
Geneva, circa 1795
Ø 57 mm; S-210

Invention of the Marine Chronometer

1600   1700   1825

A Princely Sum of Prize Money

In the early 18th century, Europe's seagoing nations vied for maritime supremacy. The ability to determine the exact location of a ship or fleet in mid-ocean was of utmost importance. But while skilled navigators could easily find their latitude (north-south position) by measuring the angle between the horizon and a known heavenly body such as the sun or North Star, they still lacked the means of determining their longitude (east-west position). Extremely precise clocks, or chronometers, were key to solving the problem, as local times and longitude are interdependent.

In 1714, the British Parliament passed the "Longitude Act," which included a "princely sum" of prize money to the inventor of a simple and practical method to accurately determine longitude on the high seas. Along with astronomers, horologists searched for solutions and developed the so-called "marine chronometer."

A large part of the coveted prize money was ultimately won by John Harrison (1693–1776). After several unsuccessful attempts, he equipped his "H4" marine chronometer with a rapidly oscillating balance with temperature compensation. In 1761, with nearly perfect precision, this timekeeper correctly showed the time at the home port of a ship throughout its voyage.

In France, the "Académie royale des sciences" offered a similar reward. The challenge was taken up by Pierre Le Roy (1717–1785), who submitted a free detent escapement and a system to compensate for temperature fluctuations. Other important competitors were the Swiss-born Ferdinand Berthoud (1727–1807) and his nephew Louis Berthoud (1754–1813). Le Roy developed a detent chronometer escapement and a system to compensate for variations in ambient temperature (page 41, S-207).

Marine chronometers, to which improvements were made over several decades, represented the height of precision timekeeping. British watchmakers pioneered and dominated the field for many years. These very expensive instruments became standard for the British Navy by around 1825. The practical method that allowed ships to navigate far from land provided the basis for new trade relationships with distant markets.

Locating Longitude

This marine chronometer, built in 1796 by Pennington and Pendleton, was based on an earlier design from 1774 of Thomas Mudge (1715–1794), the well-known London watchmaker. Mudge equipped his chronometer with a constant force escapement and submitted it for the British Parliament's "Longitude Prize," but failed to win.

After coming up short again with two similar models, Mudge died an embittered man. The Mudge line of chronometers continued under his son.

Robert Pennington and
Richard Pendleton
London, circa 1796
Ø 124 mm; S-1004

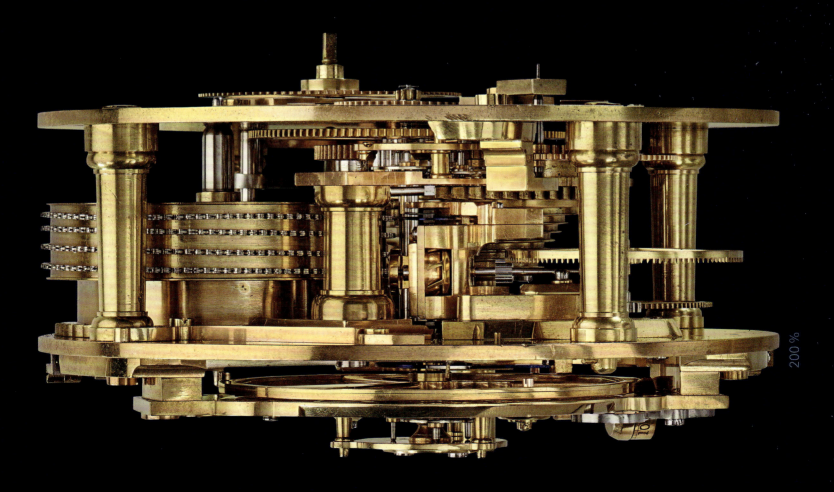

Invention of the Marine Chronometer

| 1500 | 1600 | 1700 | 1825 | 1900 |

Ferdinand Berthoud

France's first portable chronometer for determining longitude at sea was invented by Ferdinand Berthoud (1727–1807). The movement has a detent escapement and bimetallic grid used to correct for temperature fluctuations. The Swiss-born Berthoud apprenticed in Paris to Julien Le Roy (1686–1759) and in 1773 became clockmaker to the king. Both Ferdinand and his nephew Louis Berthoud competed for the longitude award of the "Académie royale des sciences."

Ferdinand Berthoud
Paris, circa 1785
Ø 60 mm; S-573

Model 76

This longitude watch, numbered "76," was constructed for Ferdinand Berthoud (1727–1807) by his pupil Jean Martin in 1804 on the model of the "No 73" invented by Berthoud in 1775. The dial is thus signed: "N° 76 / Ferdinand Berthoud Inv. / Jean Martin Exé AN 1804."

Jean Martin for Ferdinand Berthoud
Paris, 1804
Ø 69 mm; S-534

Pierre Le Roy

This pocket chronometer has a very prominent seconds hand rotating at the center, which indicates that it was intended mainly for astronomers and navigators. It was made by Pierre Le Roy (1717–1785), who entered timepieces like this one into the longitude competition that was sponsored by the Paris "Académie royale des sciences." Its anchor escapement was invented by his father Julien Le Roy (1686–1759), considered one of the most influential watchmakers of his day.

Pierre Le Roy
Paris, circa 1775
Ø 47 mm; S-207

Petite Ronde

The "Petite Ronde" by Pierre Le Roy (1717–1785) used a movement and a dial made by his father Julien Le Roy (1686–1759). The watch is shown in its gimbal within a cylindrical brass box. The whole is contained in a circular mahogany case with three brass feet to keep it level.

Pierre and Julien Le Roy
Paris, circa 1774
Ø 109 mm (wooden case); S-992

The Art of Watchmaking Conquers the Far East

Geneva's Supply Chain to China

Ever since Jesuit missionaries had brought the first timepieces and automata to China in the 16th century, these mechanical devices had fascinated the imperial court. The exotic artifacts seemed magical, sparking a general fascination with European technology. These devices offered the Jesuits the opportunity to get close to the emperor in order to advance their Christian mission.

The English led the export of timepieces to the Far East via the powerful British East India Company, which strengthened their diplomatic relationships in Asia. The timepieces were initially made in London by watchmakers like James Cox (1723–1800), William Anthony (c. 1764–1844), and William Ilbery (1772–1852), but part of their production was relocated to Switzerland. Geneva excelled in enamel painting, which was much in demand in China. Moreover, the legendary division-of-labor system of Geneva's watchmakers promised them higher profits (page 45, S-125).

The most beautiful "Chinese" watches were made in Geneva. Masterpieces were exported to the Far East by such watchmakers as Philippe-Samuel Meylan (1772–1845) and Isaac-Daniel Piguet (1775–1841). But the lack of direct contact with the Chinese market obliged Genevan makers to rely on English intermediaries. Finished products were sent first to England for export to China.

Some makers, such as Jaquet-Droz, set up a branch in London to facilitate their Far East trade.

Edouard Bovet (1797–1849), of Fleurier, was one of the Swiss watchmakers who set out to conquer the Chinese market. In 1818, he traveled to Canton, where he achieved success and established a family watchmaking dynasty. Manufacturing in Fleurier, in the canton of Neuchâtel, his company set up a branch in London, thus creating a company-controlled supply chain. His influence was so strong that "Bo Wei" became the Cantonese word for "watch" (page 43, S-989).

After peaking around 1810, the watch trade with China was interrupted by the Opium Wars (1839–1842 and 1856–1860), which stunted diplomatic and commercial relations between the British Empire and China.

Mandarin Duck

The back of this enamel-painted watch case is decorated with a mandarin duck, an appropriate image for a Chinese timekeeper. The male of the species is instantly recognizable by the two orange "sails" on its back, exaggerated in this image to artful effect. Although signed by Edouard Bovet (1797–1849), a watchmaker from the village of Fleurier in Switzerland, the movement is clearly based on one specially designed for the Chinese by English watchmaker William Ilbery (1772–1852), who owned a shop in the same village.

Most striking is the use of elegant bridges instead of plates, an innovation of the French watchmaker Jean-Antoine Lépine (1720–1814) from 1770. The narrow bridges make the movement much more accessible for assembly and repair.

Bovet
Fleurier, circa 1835
Ø 57 mm; S-989

The Art of Watchmaking Conquers the Far East

| 1500 | 1600 | 1700 | **1730** | 1840 | 1900 |

Symbol of Luck

The most beautiful "Chinese" watches were made in Geneva, Switzerland, whose craftsmen found a lucrative market in the Far East in the 18th and 19th centuries. Pearls were considered by the Chinese to be symbols of luck, and almost always, the cases and dials of watches produced for the China trade were heavily decorated with pearls.

Piguet & Meylan (watchmaker)
Frères Oltramare (casemaker)
Geneva, circa 1825
Ø 55 mm; S-154

Songbirds

In the 1770s, Swiss-born Pierre Jaquet-Droz (1721–1790) created singing mechanical birds and barking dogs. Even more astounding, he miniaturized and incorporated his automata into pocket watch cases, a feat for which he was popularly celebrated as a magician and genius. The Chinese were known to be captivated by automata and, by the late 18th century, became a major outlet for European-made watches equipped with these life-like contrivances.

Jaquet-Droz
Geneva, circa 1785
Ø 62 mm; S-410

Collaborations

This extraordinary movement, crafted in the London workshop of William Ilbery (1772–1852), demonstrates the power of collaboration between Swiss and English craftsmen. The movement is completely enameled by a Genevan craftsman and follows the case's teardrop shape.

Ilbery (watchmaker)
Jean-Louis Richter (enamel painter)
Geneva, circa 1805
W. 59 mm; S-125

The Art of Watchmaking Conquers the Far East

| 1500 | 1600 | 1700 | **1730** | 1840 | 1900 |

Music from a Disc

The ensemble of figures on this dial belong to a complex automaton. When set in motion, the musicians play their instruments. The complexity of the sound mechanism can be seen in the movement. The disc and the blades can be thought of as forerunners of modern music CDs.

Piguet & Meylan (watchmaker)
Frères Oltramare (casemaker)
Geneva, circa 1815
Ø 72 mm; S-512

Undying Love

This musical snuffbox was the perfect item for the Far Eastern market. To the Chinese, the butterfly represents undying love. About 250 pins cover each side of the disc. They pluck a total of 38 blades to produce the music.

Piguet & Meylan
Geneva, circa 1820
W. 84 mm; S-578

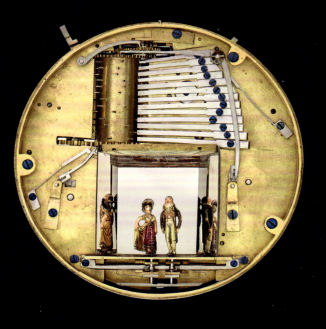

Chinese Theater

This pocket watch with music and automata has an elaborate cut-out showing figures on a miniature stage of a Chinese theater.

Piguet & Meylan
Geneva, circa 1800
Ø 62 mm; S-1040

The Art of Watchmaking Conquers the Far East

| 1500 | 1600 | 1700 | **1730** | 1840 | 1900 |

Fantasy Watches

This is an example of the "fantasy watches" produced in Geneva in the late 18th century, primarily for the Chinese market. In the Chinese tradition, the peony flower symbolizes opulence, beauty, honor, and high social status. This enamel-painted watch reproduces a colorful peony in exquisite detail. Note how the shape of the case replicates the flower's graceful contours.

Geneva, circa 1810
W. 62 mm; S-367

200 %

A Playful Curiosity

Enamel painting was also practiced in England, but it focused less on biblical or allegorical subjects and reproductions of famous paintings, and more on abstract motifs. This watch is a playful English curiosity: the chain starts as a "trompe l'oeil" enamel painting at the center of the watch case, spiraling up to the pendant point, where it continues outside the watch case as a real chain.

Stedman & Vardon
London, circa 1790
Ø 64 mm; S-756

Paired Watches for the Chinese Market

In Pursuit of Symmetry: Yin and Yang

The "Journal suisse d'horlogerie" attempts to explain China's apparent preference for timepieces in pairs: "Let us not forget how we Europeans accustomed the Chinese to wearing two watches. We never sell the models singly, but only in pairs, which are as inseparable as Siamese twins… Would you like to purchase a watch? We shall not sell it to you, unless you buy two!"

Did the Chinese actually wear two watches at once? There is no evidence to support this. More likely, Chinese customers tended to buy two identical watches at a time so that they would have a spare timepiece available if the first one should be lost or cease to function properly. Around 1800, watchmakers were quite scarce in China. The few foreign specialists who could repair timepieces and automata lived in Hong Kong or Shanghai, which often meant a journey of several days' duration for the owner. In some instances, timepieces had to be returned to Switzerland for repair. These practical considerations no doubt coincided with the love of symmetry, reflecting the opposing but complementary principles of Yin and Yang in Taoist philosophy (page 51, S-133 A+B).

English manufacturers were the first to enter the lucrative Chinese trade in identically paired watches, but Geneva's watchmakers soon followed. Swiss watches immediately gained popularity, primarily because they were handsomely decorated with miniatures painted by Genevan enamelers, such as Jean-Abraham Lissignol (1749–1819), Jean-Louis Richter (1766–1841), and Jean-François-Victor Dupont (1785–1863).

To please their Chinese clientele, these artists created elaborate mirror-image motifs for twinned watches that made the pair inseparable. The cases were adorned with beautiful renderings of mythological subjects, scenes from theater plays, or allegorical motifs. The invention of mirrored paintings and the enamelers' pursuit of perfection resulted in unique masterpieces that enhanced the reputation of Geneva's watchmakers and their luxury products.

From Geneva with Love

These two heart-shaped watches look almost identical. But look carefully and you will see they are actually mirror images in which the subjects face each other to form complementary units. This method of mirrored images on watches was a Genevan innovation. The enameling is based on a painting by Louise-Elisabeth Vigée-Le Brun (1755–1842), made in Paris circa 1780.

Piguet & Meylan (watchmaker)
Jean-Abraham Lissignol
(enamel painter)
Geneva, circa 1815
W. 66 mm; S-133 A+B

Paired Watches for the Chinese Market

Love Duel

These mirror-image pistols, named "Love Duel," are actually perfume atomizers, forerunners of today's vaporizers. Watch dials are hidden under a lid in the handles, a rare combination of watch and perfume sprayer. Pressing the trigger released an enamel flower from the barrel, giving off

Virgin without Halo

This watch made for the Chinese market features a musical automaton. The back has a twinned enamel painting based on Raphael's (1483–1520) "Madonna della Sedia," presenting the Virgin Mary with the infants Jesus and John the Baptist.
But watches destined for China removed Christian references, in this case leaving only the Madonna as an anonymous mother with her child.

Piguet & Meylan (watchmaker)
Jean-Abraham Lissignol (enamel painter)
Frères Oltramare (casemaker)
Geneva, circa 1815
Ø 44 mm; S-489 A+B

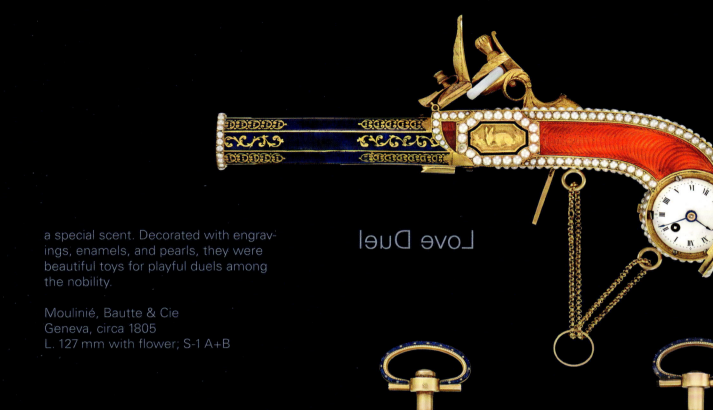

Love Duel

a special scent. Decorated with engravings, enamels, and pearls, they were beautiful toys for playful duels among the nobility.

Moulinié, Bautte & Cie
Geneva, circa 1805
L. 127 mm with flower; S-1 A+B

Mirrored Motions

The mirrored images on these paired watches were painted by Genevan enameler Jean-Louis Richter (1769–1840) after an oil painting by Claude-Joseph Vernet (1714–1789).
The movements of this pair were built by Englishman John Rich in his Geneva workshop. Rich also doubled the automaton. This is the only mirrored automaton known to exist, an extraordinary expression of Yin-Yang symmetry.

John Rich (watchmaker)
London, circa 1790
Jean-Louis Richter (enamel painter)
Geneva, circa 1790
Ø 63 mm; S-428 + S-988

Watches for the Ottoman Empire

Reckoning with the Moon

Western watches had been exported to Constantinople since the 17th century. There was even a small colony of European watchmakers in Constantinople, among them Isaac Rousseau (1672–1747), father of the philosopher Jean-Jacques Rousseau (1712–1778). Exports to the Ottoman Empire peaked around 1800.

Since Turkish life was regulated by the lunar calendar, imported timepieces often featured indications of phases and ages of the moon, and used a system of time measurement in which the day begins at sunset. This system made it easy for people to set the hands of the timepiece, since anyone can observe sunset with the naked eye. It was often the case that these watches served primarily as jewelry and badges of prestige. Genevan enamelers and case makers strengthened Switzerland's export-oriented luxury industry.

Watches built for the Ottoman market are readily identifiable by their Turkish numerals. Oval and round cases were richly decorated but always heeded the Islamic prohibition against the depiction of human beings. Instead of pure calligraphy, images of landscapes, such as views of the Bosphorus or military trophies, could be found. Pink, red, and green tones predominated on enameled cases. Often watches were paired with a mirror, a spyglass, or a little receptacle for smelling salts, called a "vinaigrette."

In the second half of the 18th century, foreign watchmakers living in Constantinople began returning to Europe, because of the availability of trained craftsmen there. At the time, most watches for the Turkish market were manufactured in London. A few English makers even specialized in this trade, notably Markwick, Markham & Borell, active in London from 1793 to 1813. In France, Abraham-Louis Breguet (1747–1823) also produced watches with distinctive cases and dials for Ottoman customers. To facilitate trade onsite, around 1811 his company dispatched its own commercial representative to Constantinople (page 56, S-235).

Singing Birds

Between 1810 and 1835 Frères Rochat had a workshop in Geneva. They were exceptionally gifted in fabricating complicated watches with automata, especially with singing birds. This watch with its Turkish numerals on the dial was made for the Ottoman market. Watch cases were richly decorated but always heeded the Islamic prohibition against the depiction of human beings. Instead, images of landscapes or military trophies could be found.

Frères Rochat
Geneva, circa 1820
Ø 63 mm; S-1106

Watches for the Ottoman Empire

| 1500 | 1600 | 1700 | **1750** | 1850 | 1900 |

For Napoleon

This quarter-repeating pocket watch was made by Breguet & Fils in 1807 for the Ottoman market and sold to the Turkish ambassador in Paris, who gave it as a present to Napoleon (1769–1821). The red enameled case features an Islamic star and crescent, rendered in radiant guilloché.

Breguet & Fils (watchmaker)
Jean-Louis Joly (casemaker)
Paris, 1807
Ø 57 mm; S-235

Islamic Motifs

This watch, made for the Ottoman market, has three embedded cases, each exquisitely enameled. Normally such protective cases were very simple, serving only a practical purpose. Ottoman as well as Chinese customers, however, preferred this sort of ultimate adornment, which European craftsmen proudly accommodated.

Markwick, Markham & Borell
London, circa 1810
Ø 49 mm; S-750

Mapping the Empire

In order to appeal to Turkish clients, the back of this watch case is decorated with an enameled map called "The Ottoman Empire." It shows the Eastern Mediterranean with names given in Perso-Arabic calligraphy. The dial uses Ottoman Turkish numerals.

Geneva, circa 1825
Ø 51 mm; S-451

Musical Mirror

Made in Geneva, this mirror contains a music mechanism that plays two melodies on demand. Although the piece does not contain a watch, the music mechanism was made by watchmakers. On the back is an enameled landscape titled "Straits of Bosphorus." But the scene looks more like the surroundings of Geneva than the Turkish countryside. The Genevan enameler Jacques-Marc Henry probably had never visited Constantinople.

Jacques-Marc Henry (enamel painter)
Geneva, circa 1820
W. 158 mm; S-317

Breathing Life into Machines

The Magic World of Automata

The Age of Enlightenment was known for a scientific and mechanistic view of the world. The French physician and philosopher Julien Offray de La Mettrie (1709–1751) claimed in 1748 that human beings operated like machines. In the spirit of the epoch and inspired by the early automata of the Renaissance, Swiss watchmakers of the period constructed breathtaking miniature automata.

The animated scenes featured in these timepieces ranged from figurines that moved their arms to indicate the time to complex mechanisms depicting pastoral scenes, theatrical plays, or chamber concerts, full of motion and machine music. Enthusiasm for these "tableaux vivants" was so strong that watches were often purchased just for their automata. The same was true for various other items, such as perfume flacons, mirrors, or snuffboxes equipped with these exquisite mechanisms (page 61, S-770).

Geneva's watchmakers specialized in singing-bird automata. These mechanical marvels used tiny organ pipes to replicate birdsong. Pierre Jaquet-Droz (1721–1790) and his son Henri-Louis (1752–1791), along with their partners Jean-Frédéric Leschot (1746–1824) and Jacob Frisard (1753–1812), were the undisputed masters of the craft. Eventually they invented flutes with sliding pistons to enhance the sound quality. The Frères Rochat and Charles-Abraham Bruguier (1788–1862) fabricated singing-bird automata until around 1850. Their masterpieces are represented in museums and collections around the world.

In early automata, only bells created the sound, while later improvements used programmed cylinders or discs that caused a set of tuned teeth to vibrate like a musical instrument. Henri-Daniel Capt (1773– after 1837), Isaac-Daniel Piguet (1775–1841), and Philippe-Samuel Meylan (1772–1845) developed this art to perfection.

These magical worlds, where birds never stopped singing and fountains endlessly gurgled, might be seen as precursors of today's ubiquitous portable media players. Well before the age of motion pictures, these colorful little animated stages amused audiences as they spread rapidly across European and Chinese markets.

Blue Cage

The "Blue Cage" features a single, gorgeously plumed singing-bird automaton, driven by a series of rotating cams that control the colorful bird's movements and the pitch of its whistle. The acoustic quality was a significant improvement over the usual serinettes.

Frères Rochat
Geneva, circa 1810
H. 195 mm; S-628

Breathing Life into Machines

| 1500 | 1600 | 1700 | **1730** | 1860 | 1900 |

On Stage

This telescope is equipped with an automaton, a watch, and music. On a stage below the dial, miniature figures dance to music in a fascinating pocket drama, charming European audiences of the day. The uncovered movement reveals the backstage machinery behind the magic, including a rotating cylinder programmed with pins that cause tuned teeth to vibrate musically.

Piguet & Capt
Geneva, circa 1805
Ø 48 mm; S-166

Barking Dog

This watch is one of a limited series on the theme of a dog barking at a swan. The hours and quarters sound with the barking of the dog. A tiny bellows blows and a whistle produces various sounds as the dog moves its head. The automaton is based on a 1731 painting by French Rococo artist Jean-Baptiste Oudry (1686–1755).

Piguet & Meylan
Geneva, circa 1820
Ø 60 mm; S-1010

Love Letters

This exquisitely ornamented snuffbox, of a genre known as "objects of virtue," presents a chamber concert played by automata. All the figures are animated, including the monkey playing the triangle as the figures on the left applaud. At the bottom of the piece is a secret compartment, just the right place to conceal a love letter.

Antoine Rojard
Geneva, circa 1810
W. 87 mm; S-770

Breathing Life into Machines

1500   1600   1700   **1730**   1860   1900

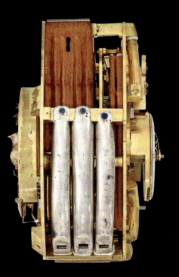

Scent of Opulence

Singing-bird automata were a huge fad in the 18th century. Brought to life by the great Pierre Jaquet-Droz (1721–1790), the one in this heavily ornamented scent flask performs a complicated choreography to the tune of a small organ pipe which produces its song.

The opulent piece was typical of automata made for the Chinese market.

Jaquet-Droz & Leschot
Jacob Frisard
Geneva, 1786
H. 160 mm; S-1006

Breathing Life into Machines

1500　　1600　　1700　**1730**　　　　1860　1900

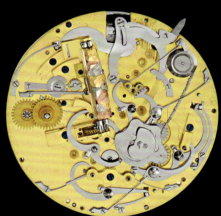

175%

Mechanical Moses

Equipped with one of the most complex automata ever made for a timepiece of its size, this watch reenacts a biblical scene in which a mechanical Moses strikes a rock with his staff, releasing a rush of water, simulated by two twisting glass rods. The thirsty figures around him reach out to catch the water. In the smaller oval frame, two cherubs strike the hours and quarters.

Dubois & Fils
Le Locle, circa 1815
Ø 67 mm; S-195

Musical Figures

Pierre-Simon Gounouilhou found a way to embed automata in a small, flat musical movement. His discovery was an adaptation of the "comb music box," which used a small comb with tuned steel blades instead of bells. Moving to the music were the grazing cow and goat and the woman playing a guitar for the man on the bridge. In the movement there are other figures lined up on a moving chain to take his place.

Pierre-Simon Gounouilhou
Geneva, circa 1800
Ø 64 mm; S-315

Bird on the Wrist

This unique bracelet, decorated in gold and champlevé enamel, houses a singing mechanical bird. When the automaton is activated, the colorful nightingale jumps out, to the delight of the wearer and her friends. It turns, flaps its wings, and breaks into song.

Frères Rochat (watchmaker)
Charles-Abraham Bruguier I (automata maker)
Geneva, circa 1825
W. 64 mm; S-174

Pioneers of Modern Watchmaking

Abraham-Louis Breguet's Horological Genius

In watchmaking, a few individuals stand apart for their extraordinary virtuosity, but none more than Abraham-Louis Breguet (1747–1823), unanimously acknowledged as the absolute master of the craft.

Born in 1747 in Neuchâtel in Switzerland, Breguet was first trained by his stepfather as a watchmaker. At the age of fifteen, he was sent to Versailles and Paris to complete his training—beginning one of the most remarkable careers of his generation. In 1775, Breguet opened his own workshop on the Quai de l'Horloge and quickly became famous for his technical skills and creativity. It was there that he developed the most complicated watch of his day, the Grand Complication No. 160, commissioned for Queen Marie-Antoinette.

In 1793, the political and social instability of the French Revolution forced Breguet to leave France and return to Switzerland, where he stayed until the nightmare in Paris was over. Two years later, he returned to Paris brimming with new ideas and a zest for action.

A virtuoso watchmaker, Breguet transformed many of his ideas into reality. His innovations included the constant-force escapement; the tourbillon, which compensates for imbalances in the escapement; and the "pare-chute" system, a kind of shock absorber. Breguet also profoundly influenced the aesthetics of timepieces. Elegance and simplicity characterized his movements, cases, and dials. By shunning unnecessary decoration and prioritizing the creation of purely practical devices, he became the godfather of the simple watch, an exemplar of "form follows function" (page 69, S-1026).

Breguet was in contact with other talented horologists, including Jean-Antoine Lépine (1720–1814) and Antide Janvier (1751–1835). Lépine constructed thinner watches by redesigning the movement. Janvier and Breguet both experimented with double pendulums to increase clock accuracy. Eventually, Breguet built a pocket watch that communicated overnight with a table clock, which automatically wound the pocket watch, synchronized its hands, and adjusted the frequency of the balance—a seamless mechanical combination that worked without human hands.

In Harmony

Abraham-Louis Breguet (1747–1823) was very excited about his invention of the "Sympathique," a paired clock-watch device designed to wind and set the watch automatically. When the watch is put into the special cradle of the master clock at three o'clock a.m., two rods enter the watch movement to complete the robotic operation. This was a technical feat that no other watchmaker in the world could match.

Abraham-Louis Breguet (pocket watch)
Paris, before 1823
Ø 49 mm; S-970 B

Breguet Neveu & Cie (table clock)
Paris, 1836
H. 625 mm; S-970 A

Pioneers of Modern Watchmaking

1500   1600   1700   **1750**   1850   1900

Touching Time

The "Tactile Pocket Watch," a tour de force of practicality and aesthetics by the great Abraham-Louis Breguet (1747–1823), made time palpable. It was considered impolite to look at one's watch in company. This ingenious watch allowed the wearer to secretly check the time by feel, even when it was carried deep in the pocket.

Abraham-Louis Breguet
Paris, circa 1800
Ø 50 mm; S-234

Visual Feast

The dials of Jean-Antoine Lépine (1720–1814) are visual masterpieces. This one presents an invented combination of Roman and Arabic numerals that conveys a feeling of balance and harmony. It also gives the "equation of time," indicating the difference between "solar time" and "mean time."

Jean-Antoine Lépine (watchmaker)
Guillaume Mermillod (casemaker)
Paris, 1789
Ø 61 mm; S-533

Perpétuelle

This "Perpétuelle" was one of the most sophisticated watches Abraham-Louis Breguet (1747–1823) ever made. It includes an equation of time indicator, a calendar for day and month, a power-reserve indicator, and an "à toc" quarter repeater. Though Breguet did not himself invent the self-winding mechanism, he perfected it with a platinum weight that responds to the slightest motion.

Abraham-Louis Breguet
Paris, circa 1800
Ø 55 mm; S-1026

Self-Winding Watches

1500　1600　1700　**1775　1810**　1900

A Historical Mystery

Watchmaking history is still being written with respect to self-winding watches. The oldest known to date, on display at the Patek Philippe Museum, was constructed in 1778 (page 72, S-187). When the watch wearer moved, a weight in the movement was set in motion, thus tensioning the mainspring. Could it have been the world's first self-winding watch? As the movement is unsigned, some mystery remains.

In 1952, Alfred Chapuis and Eugène Jaquet, pioneer historians of Swiss watchmaking, attributed the invention of the self-winding watch to the Swiss watchmaker Abraham-Louis Perrelet (1729–1826). They based their attribution on a letter written by the Genevan naturalist Horace-Bénédict de Saussure (1740–1799) in 1777, but they failed to consider that several self-winding mechanisms had been developed more or less simultaneously during this period. It is improbable that all had been designed by the same watchmaker.

Two varieties of self-winding movements appear to have been developed prior to 1780: movements containing a rotor, a centrally pivoting weight; and movements with a rocking weight. Rotors are not suitable for pocket watches, which work best with rocking weights. But 200 years later, rotors had a renaissance with the patent for the invention of self-winding wristwatches.

Expert opinion about priority began to shift in 1993, when Joseph Flores, a historian of horology, discovered a report dating from 1778 addressed to the "Académie royale des sciences" in Paris. This document states that Hubert Sarton (1748–1828), a watchmaker from Liège in Belgium, had developed a self-winding watch with a rotor. Since the text includes a drawing (page 72) of the aforementioned watch shown in the Patek Philippe Museum, there is a high probability that Sarton had constructed it. Except for Horace-Bénédict de Saussure's 1777 letter, there is no other evidence pointing to Abraham-Louis Perrelet. Simultaneous independent discovery is not uncommon in the history of invention, but Sarton's drawing has the quality of an official patent application.

Swinging Movement

French watchmaker Jean-Charles Oudin (1768–1840) produced this experimental self-winding watch, in which the motion of the movement itself winds the mainspring. Oudin, who had apprenticed with Abraham-Louis Breguet (1747–1823), was awarded an honorable mention at the 1806 Paris Exhibition of Products of French Industry for this creative approach to automatic winding.

Jean-Charles Oudin
Paris, 1806
Ø 59 mm; S-703

Self-Winding Watches

1500　　　1600　　　1700　　　1775　1810　　　1900

Rotating Motion

Although this watch is undated and unsigned, there is convincing evidence that it was made by Hubert Sarton (1748–1828), presumptive inventor of the self-winding mechanism. It has two major innovations: a plate-mounted rotor and inverter wheels which allow the rotor to wind up the mainspring in both directions of rotation.

Hubert Sarton
Belgium, 1778
Ø 46 mm; S-187

Drawing from 1778 by Hubert Sarton.

Rocking Motion

Oscillating Weights

This watch is most likely the earliest surviving self-winding timepiece made by the Swiss-born watchmaker Louis Recordon (1756–1826), who worked in London. He had one of the earliest patents for self-winders. His lateral winding system applied more torque to the mainspring, thus requiring less motion by the wearer.

Louis Recordon
Paris, circa 1780
Ø 57 mm; S-625

The invention of an improved self-winding watch made daily manual winding obsolete. The Swiss watchmaker Pierre Jaquet-Droz (1721–1790), famous for his singing birds and androids, developed his own version of a self-winding system, which placed two oscillating masses, bearing the maker's signature, at the edge of the watch: one wound the mainspring, the other the sounding mechanism.

Jaquet-Droz
Geneva, circa 1785
Ø 65 mm; S-115

Watches Adapt to the Modern World

Changing Times

In 1793, the French Revolutionary government instituted decimal time, which divided each day into 10 hours, each hour into 100 minutes, and each minute into 100 seconds. Everything was decimal: coins, measurements, weights, and the calendar. The decimal system was designed to make time measurement simpler and more rational. Its introduction symbolized the practical application of Enlightenment thinking to everyday life. But the new system proved difficult to implement, since people had been trained over centuries to read the angle of the hands on a 12-hour dial and could not get used to the new images of decimal time. The revolutionaries revoked decimal time sixteen months after its introduction (page 76, S-792).

This period also saw the creation of watches displaying multiple local times, reflecting a global view of the world. The ability to reliably navigate the oceans had broadened horizons for merchants and travelers. Early models indicated local times in some fifty cities (page 76, S-952).

The trend toward standardized measurement, along with the growth of scientific research, particularly in astronomy, encouraged the production of special watches. Watches for researchers were equipped with various measuring instruments, each with its own dial. Among these were thermometers in Celsius, Fahrenheit, or Réaumur.

Watches which indicated planetary movements showed that their owners were proudly broadening their knowledge. Venus's rare passages in front of the sun—so-called "transits of Venus"— were the subject of a vast international scientific effort in 1769 to use the observations to measure the size of the solar system. This spectacle launched an era of science education, boosting the popularity of pocket-watch planetaria.

The social and cultural changes of the Enlightenment were also mirrored in how watches displayed the time. Dials were built with "wandering hours," or hands that changed length. One of the most remarkable pieces was designed by Benjamin Franklin (1706–1790), who devised a hand with a tip that followed a spiral path (page 77, S-443).

Dials for keeping track of the plethora of local times gained importance in 1825, when the first steam-powered passenger railway in the world began to operate in England between Stockton and Darlington. Standard time zones that we have today did not exist yet.

Pocket Planetarium

Watchmaker Jacob Auch (1765–1842), who worked with the best astronomers of his time, is credited with miniaturizing a gigantic planetarium to the size of a pocket watch, here on the back of a watch case. The sun occupies the center of the blue enameled disc. The orbits of Mercury, Venus, Earth, and the moon with its phases are also represented.

Jacob Auch
Stuttgart, circa 1790
Ø 59 mm; S-974

Watches Adapt to the Modern World

Revolutionary Time

This unconventional watch has four hands, which show the time in both the traditional 2×12 hours in Roman numerals and the French Revolutionary decimal time from 1 to 10. Midnight would then be at ten o'clock in decimal time.

France, circa 1795
Ø 53 mm; S-792

World Timer

It is said that the Russian tsar gave this "world timer" to renowned scientist and explorer Alexander von Humboldt (1769–1859). The silver disc displays the names of 52 different locations. The disc turns once in 24 hours, indicating the differences between their local times. It is signed by its Polish inventor, but the movement was made by the famous Abraham-Louis Breguet (1747–1823).

Leon Kuchajewski
Warsaw, 1814
Ø 64 mm; S-952

Time Spiral

Based on Benjamin Franklin's spiral-hand concept, the single hand on this pocket watch makes a complete rotation every four hours. It becomes longer as it rotates. After making three revolutions and arriving at XII at the outer end of the spiral, it jumps back from long to short.

Neuchâtel Mountains, circa 1790
Ø 56 mm; S-443

Annual Calendar

The center in blue is surrounded by zodiac signs and the equation of time on an annual calendar arranged on a five-turn spiral. The calendar hand lengthens and shortens as it moves through the days of the year. Although the movement looks complicated, this is actually the simplest way for the watch's calendar to track the different lengths of each month.

Andrew Dickie
London, circa 1760
Ø 52 mm; S-1032

Three Scales

More and more, watches were outfitted for scientific study. This thermometer was an experiment by Jacques-Frédéric Houriet (1743–1830) and Urban Jürgensen (1776–1830), a Swiss and a Danish watchmaker, to fit a modern bimetallic thermometer into a regular watch case. The thermometer has the three scales: Fahrenheit, Celsius, and Réaumur.

Jacques-Frédéric Houriet
Urban Jürgensen
Le Locle, circa 1815
Ø 62 mm; S-509

Watches Adapt to the Modern World

1500　　1600　　1700　　**1790　1825**　　1900

Perpetual Calendar

This calendar watch with the first perpetual calendar ever built has a window with a rotating disc that scrolls the name of each month with its number of days. A still smaller disc under February rotates once every four years, with four adjustment positions for a full turn: three for 28 days and one for 29, accounting for leap years.

Thomas Mudge
London, 1762
Ø 50 mm; S-1033

Sky Map

The dial of this pocket watch represents a sky map of the Northern Hemisphere for January 17. There are a moon hand and a sun hand, which shows the date. The tail of the dragon-shaped hand points to the signs of the zodiac. The overlapping of the three hands indicates a solar or lunar eclipse.

George Margetts
London, 1778
Ø 58 mm; S-1055

Geocentric

This geocentric planetarium has black lines radiating from Earth to the signs of the zodiac and steel hands to the sun and moon. The dial revolves once per year. The horizontal steel bar is the horizon. The sun is moving toward sunset, and the moon has set and is already below the horizon. It is calculated to the latitude of Stuttgart, the watchmaker's location.

Jacob Auch
Stuttgart, circa 1790
Ø 68 mm; S-1057

Sundial

In this watch, the sun reigns supreme at the center of the dial, with all four hands pointing toward it. Pushing the pendant causes the hands to jump instantly to subsidiary dials, indicating the current hour, minute, day of the week, and day of the month.

Dubois & Fils
Le Locle, circa 1790
Ø 58 mm; S-333

1600   1700   1780   1890

Form Watches as Fashion Statements

In the final decades of the 18th century, extravagant designs came into fashion for ladies' timepieces; they were now built in a vast range of shapes, from insects and other animals, flowers, and fruits to musical instruments, shoes, and hats. Enamel painting of cases had a renaissance in Geneva, while dials displaying time retreated from view.

Masters of miniaturization, Geneva's watchmakers and goldsmiths were well positioned to produce these flights of horological fancy, which appealed especially to female customers of the emerging middle class.

Aesthetic appeal became more important than accuracy, so movements were mechanically simple, with few if any complications. Some were integrated into such personal accessories as snuffboxes, fans, perfume bottles, pencils, or lorgnettes. The period also saw the rise of smaller pocket watches worn as pendants or brooches. Most were adorned with pearls, gemstones, or enamel paintings. Popular ornamental techniques included guilloché, champlevé enamel, and various engravings.

Although Geneva was the center for the production of "form watches," they were also made in Paris, London, and Vienna. Some Austrian watchmakers purchased Geneva-made movements, intending to mount them in their own cases and signing them with their own names.

The demand for form watches declined after 1840, only to revive some fifty years later. That decade also saw the rise of Art Nouveau, which would inspire richly decorated watches of fanciful shapes used as fashion accessories.

Hats Off!

When closed, this pendant watch resembles the hat of perhaps a military officer or government official. The decorative enamel and pearls testify to high rank.

Geneva, circa 1795
W. 38 mm; S-49

Ornamental Watches for Women

This gold pendant watch, shaped like a bow and arrow, is decorated with pearls. The enamel painting on the back of the case depicts a cherub nestled in a battle helmet.

Geneva, circa 1810
W. 53 mm; S-71

Love's Arrow

Pop-up

The pearls of this oyster-shell watch are on the outside rather than the inside of the shell, from where a watch pops up when the shell is opened. The gold case is enameled in green and black and also decorated with semi-precious stones.

Geneva, circa 1815
Ø 29 mm; S-35

The watch becomes a women's fashion accessory. With timekeeping secondary, the movements are very simple. The outline of the case of this gold pendant watch, lavishly painted in enamel, is identical for the images on both front and back, the sheep and the sheepdog. Each wears a pearl necklace.

Geneva, circa 1815
W. 33 mm; S-31

Reversible

Sweet Cherub

Its neck ringed with three strings of pearls, this sweet cherub with two different faces covers an enameled gold watch with center seconds.

Geneva, circa 1815
W. 47 mm; S-70

1600   1700   1820   1900

From Striking to Music Players

English watchmakers played an important role in the invention of repeater watches, which chime the time in response to the push of a button. Daniel Quare (1648–1724) received a patent in London for a watch with a quarter repeater in 1687. This innovation enabled the owner of a repeater watch to know the time in the dark without having to light an oil lamp or candle (page 86, S-1017).

Several types of repeater watches were developed, beginning with the quarter repeater, which strikes the hours and quarter hours on demand. It was followed by the seven-and-a-half-minute, five-minute, and minute repeater. The earliest watches in this genre had small hammers that struck a bell. Later, the bells were replaced by rods of tempered steel, called gongs, which opened the way for thinner watches. Their makers had to have a well-trained ear for music to tune the gongs.

A special version of the repeater watch, called "montre à toc," had been manufactured since the late 17th century. Its hammer struck directly against the inside of the case, replacing the chimes with muffled vibrations that could be felt in the hand. Some repeaters were fitted with a pin that protruded from the case and pulsated quietly when the finger touched it. Known as "montres à tact," these mechanisms solved a problem of etiquette, as it was considered terribly impolite to look at one's watch in the presence of another person. The French word "tact," which means "sense of touch," thus gave rise to the English word "tactful" (page 86, S-871).

The oldest watches with musical mechanisms were manufactured in London in the first half of the 18th century. Their sound was initially produced by hammers striking against bells and later by steel blades set into vibration by pins mounted on moving cylinders or discs. In time, these watches became thinner. In Geneva they were perfected around 1800.

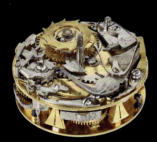

This watch has a quarter repeater, which produces sound on demand. Based on a "rack and snail" mechanism, it was one of the first efficient and reliable repeaters. This watch is equipped with a second protective case, which also amplifies the sound of the bell. Its maker, Thomas Tompion (1639–1713), was nicknamed "the father of English watchmaking."

Tompion & Banger
London, circa 1705
Ø 55 mm; S-1009

Sound on Demand

Time Made Audible

This movement has two independent gear trains: one for striking the time when the minute hand reaches the full hour or the quarters. It can be turned off and on with a lever on the outside of the bezel. The other gear train is for repeating the time on demand. A bell in the case makes time audible.

Daniel Quare
London, circa 1710
Ø 59 mm; S-1017

Self-Striking and Repeating

This diamond-studded pocket watch features a "dumb" quarter repeater—meaning it does not chime. Its hammers strike the inside of the case instead, producing a muffled sound that can be felt in the palm of the hand for discreet checks of the time. The watchmaker's patron was Marie Leszczyńska (1703–1768), the wife of Louis XV (1710–1774) and queen of France.

Jean-Baptiste Baillons
Paris, circa 1770
Ø 51 mm; S-871

Touch and Feel

Made around 1770, this may well be the earliest watch movement to play a melody with tuned steel blades rather than bells. It was driven and programmed by a pinned cylinder. The movement is signed, originally in French: "The instrument was invented and executed by Ransonet in Nancy."

Michel Joseph Ransonet
Nancy, circa 1770
Ø 46 mm; S-561

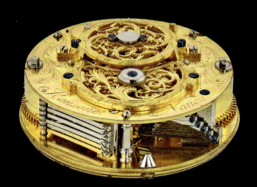

Play Me a Melody

This pocket watch with minute repeater sounds the time to the minute on demand. At 12:59, chiming goes on for about 20 seconds. Flip up the back cover and the movement's intricately beautiful striking mechanism is made completely visible.

Piguet & Meylan
Geneva, circa 1821
Ø 56 mm; S-831

Chime the Minute

Measuring the Smallest Time Units

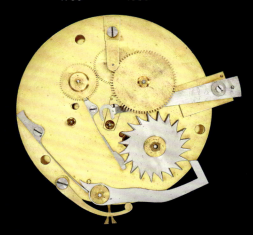

Tenths, Hundredths, and Thousandths of a Second

Precision measurement of speed requires knowing the exact time needed to cover a given distance. The first speedometers were pedometers coupled with a timekeeper. Portable versions became available for trouser pockets and saddlebags.

Time and speed were paramount concerns in the Industrial Revolution. Increasing the accuracy of timekeepers was the great challenge in the age of the steam engine and the railroad. Timepieces could soon measure fractions of seconds beyond one fifth: Tenths, hundredths, and thousandths of a second were the watchwords of a society ever more preoccupied with speed.

After velocities became precisely recordable, the fastest time across the finish line in a competition could now be registered for a world record.

Sporting events, especially horse races, depended on these new, more accurate timekeepers. Noting the increasing popularity of equestrian sports, Nicolas Mathieu Rieussec (1781–1866) produced a timepiece in 1821 that could measure the placement of finishers in horse races. Combining in its name the Greek words "chronos" (time) and "graphein" (to write), Rieussec's "chronograph" could be triggered to deposit a droplet of ink on its dial as each horse crossed the finish line (page 90, S-965; page 91, S-878).

Rieussec soon miniaturized his mechanism and integrated it into a pocket watch case to make the device portable. The hand for the seconds at the center has a tiny container of ink on its tip. When a button in the pendant is pressed, a small drop of ink is deposited directly on the dial, thus recording the elapsed time. The dial has to be wiped after each use.

With the fast-growing popularity during the 19th century of speed sports like horse and bicycle racing, chronographs were increasingly in demand. They could make a champion in a fraction of a second!

Writing Time

This inking chronograph (time-writer), an early version of a stopwatch, does not function as a regular watch. Rather, when activated by a push-button at the bottom, the hand for seconds marks with ink the elapsed time. It also shows time intervals in hours and minutes.

Breguet Neveux & Cie
Paris, 1845
Ø 79 mm; S-825

Measuring the Smallest Time Units

1500　　　　　　　　1700　　　　　1780　　1830　　　　1900

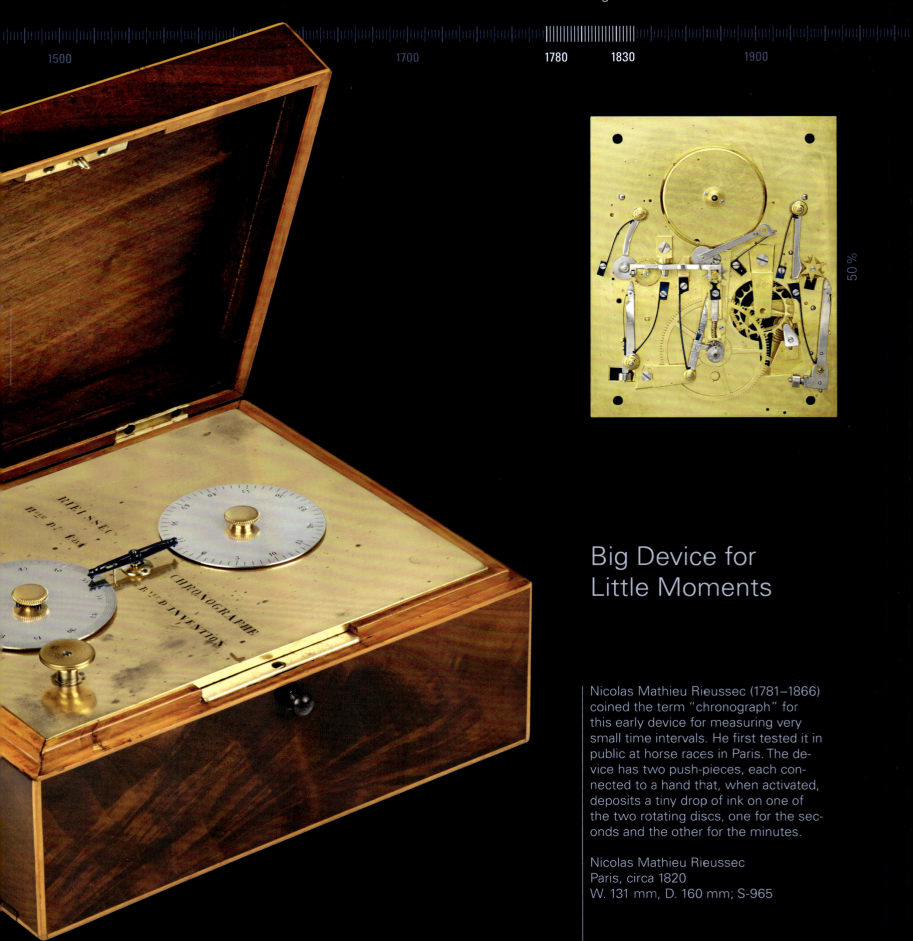

50 %

Big Device for Little Moments

Nicolas Mathieu Rieussec (1781–1866) coined the term "chronograph" for this early device for measuring very small time intervals. He first tested it in public at horse races in Paris. The device has two push-pieces, each connected to a hand that, when activated, deposits a tiny drop of ink on one of the two rotating discs, one for the seconds and the other for the minutes.

Nicolas Mathieu Rieussec
Paris, circa 1820
W. 131 mm, D. 160 mm; S-965

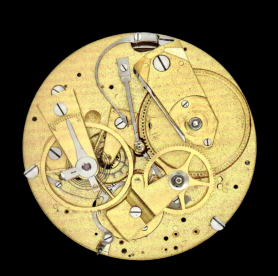

Portable Inking Chronograph

Nicolas Mathieu Rieussec (1781–1866) managed to fit his chronograph into a watch case, making it portable. It can act like a regular watch and also like a stopwatch by pressing buttons at the crown. It is capable of measuring seconds but, unlike his earlier device, cannot record the results.

Nicolas Mathieu Rieussec
Paris, 1842
Ø 68 mm; S-878

Shrinking the Chronometer

The escapement with the swinging balance determines a watch's accuracy. In the 18th century, European watchmakers focused on improving this regulating device. Increasing the frequency of the balance also increases precision by virtue of shorter time intervals: fifths of a second now became standard.

The most accurate pocket watches, using new types of escapements, came out of the workshop of John Arnold (1736–1799) in London. One of his timepieces was used on a ship of the British East India Company en route to India in 1777. Its navigational applications were emphasized in a 1779 pamphlet, "Some notes useful to those who have Chronometers at Sea." This publication marked the first appearance of the term "chronometer," the standard term for high-precision timepieces. Eventually, timepieces had to undergo special, independent tests before they could be called chronometers (page 93, S-1034).

Various escapements were developed in Switzerland by Antoine Tavan (1749–1836) and others. Inspired by Englishman Thomas Mudge's lever escapement, the Genevan watchmaker Jean-Moïse Pouzait (1753–1793) developed an early version of the "Swiss lever escapement," still found today in most mechanical watches.

Around 1776, Pouzait also designed a way to stop and start the seconds hand on a movement with a very slow, swinging balance of one tick per second (page 94, S-378).

Indication of seconds became increasingly common, and not only for timekeepers designed for navigators. In the industrial age, faster production times required more precise time measurement, which became equally useful in scientific research.

Watches were produced in increasing quantities and improved quality not only in England and Switzerland, but also in the U.S.A. and elsewhere.

By the middle of the 19th century, Switzerland became the leading watchmaking country in world.

Splendid Accuracy

This movement showcases the technical beauty of John Arnold's (1736–1799) patented balances, considered the most accurate in the world. Temperature compensation is achieved through two bimetallic loops, resembling shoelace bows, which is called the "S-Type."

Note the filigree on the piece securing the circular balance to the top plate.

John Arnold
London, 1781
Ø 74 mm; S-1034

High-Precision Watches

| 1500 | 1600 | 1700 | 1750 | 1850 | 1900 |

Swiss Provenance

The movement's very large balance wheel, fully visible through the glass on the back of the case, oscillates slowly, causing the second hand to literally jump from one second to the next with each swing of the balance. This so-called "jump second" allowed scientists to make very precise time measurements.

Jean-Moïse Pouzait
Geneva, 1782
Ø 80 mm; S-378

American Pioneer

This is probably the first watch based on British technology that was made entirely on American soil. It features an improved escapement and separates the calendar gear from the going train to avoid disturbances, a technical solution not previously known in Europe.

Henry Voight
Philadelphia, 1780
Ø 55 mm; S-1022

German Revival

This pocket chronometer, made around 1820 by Johann Christian Friedrich Gutkaes (1785–1845), marked a revival in German watchmaking. It is fitted with a spring-detent escapement and a regulator dial with a large hand for the seconds. The science-minded Gutkaes was particularly interested in making precision timekeepers for astronomers.

Johann Christian Friedrich Gutkaes
Dresden, circa 1820
Ø 58 mm; S-1038

Eclecticism and Historicism

Old versus New versus Old

An eclectic mingling of styles from different periods was a hallmark of a 19th-century movement known as Historicism. It exerted a powerful influence on the crafts, including watchmaking, even though skilled handwork was already being displaced by the new machines of the Industrial Revolution.

In Geneva, center of the luxury industries, pocket watches continued to be made using centuries-old local techniques such as enamel painting. After Geneva became part of the Swiss Confederation in 1815, some pocket watches were decorated with enamel miniatures depicting patriotic themes, such as the coats-of-arms and traditional costumes of the cantons. These pieces were much sought after by affluent tourists, and locals as well.

Historicist ornamentation looked back to the Middle Ages, the Renaissance, the Baroque and the Rococo periods. The engraver's stylus, or burin, was applied with great skill and exactness to the enamel work in the old champlevé or new taille d'épargne techniques. The designs were hand-engraved with such precision that they were easily confused with machine-made products.

In fact, such confusion may not have been accidental, as craftsmen were increasingly schooled in the machine-age aesthetic. Ironically, this emulation of machine precision is what, to an expert eye, clearly distinguishes such 19th-century "neo-styles" as Neo-Gothic and Neo-Renaissance from their originals.

One of the exemplars of Historicism was the interior decoration of the Crystal Palace for the 1851 Great Exhibition in London. The first-ever World Exposition, it became the global showroom for the products and eclectic styles of its time.

Patriotic Themes

This watch was offered as a prize at the Basel Federal Shooting Competition in 1844, which coincided with the 400th anniversary celebration of the Battle of Saint Jacob. A patriotic scene of the event appears in a rectangular cartouche on the back of the case. This is a very early example of such presentation timepieces, known as "Schützenuhren"—shooting watches.

François & Auguste Meylan
Geneva, 1840
Ø 43 mm; S-997

Eclecticism and Historicism

| 1500 | 1600 | 1700 | 1815 | 1860 | 1900 |

Skeleton Watch

Ironically, this minimalist "skeleton watch," with the main plate and bridges cut back and made of transparent rock crystal to make the inner workings as visible as possible, resembles the ornate Historicist pieces of the period. To maximize transparency, the dial was reduced to numerals on the outer band. Its watchmaker was a member of a Swiss colony in Poland.

Olivier Delachaux
Lustsevek, Poland, 1821
Ø 56 mm; S-736

Wanderlust

In the late 18th century, travel around Europe became a popular leisure and educational activity. New developments in cartography and road networks made travel much easier and faster. Maps were often reproduced on watch cases, here those of Prussia and the Baltic Sea. Also note the modern dial, with indication of jumping hours and wandering minutes in the two apertures.

Ravené
Berlin, circa 1820
Ø 49 mm; S-883

98

Orientalism

This bracelet fitted with a watch, named "Alhambra," reflected the 19th century's fad for "orientalism." This is one of the earliest known wristwatches. Although signed by Thueux, a retailer in Paris, it was most likely made in Geneva around 1840 by one of Jean-François Bautte's (1772–1837) companies.

Jean-François Bautte & Cie
Geneva, circa 1840
W. 46 mm; S-380

Jumping Hours

The rich, eclectic pattern of this watch case is a beautiful example of the "taille d'épargne" technique. The time is displayed in an aperture, behind which a disc rotates for the hours and another for the minutes. This watch also features jumping hours and "wandering minutes."

Geneva, circa 1840
Ø 43 mm; S-913

Crowning of the Pocket Watch

Revolution in Winding and Setting Watches

Until around 1850, pocket watches required the use of a key to wind them and set their hands to the right time. To wind the watch, the key was inserted in a hole either in the back of the case or in the dial. To set the time, the same key was placed on the shaft of the minute hand. Damage to the dial, case, or hands was not unusual, and the key could easily be lost.

By 1750, watchmakers were seeking ways to eliminate the key. The first attempts date from the second half of the 18th century, when master watchmakers such as John Arnold (1736–1799) in London (page 103, S-864) and Abraham-Louis Breguet (1747–1823) in Paris developed watches that could be wound with a push-piece or pendant. Setting the hands still required a key, however. It was time for a better solution.

A young French watchmaker named Jean Adrien Philippe (1815–1894) achieved the technological breakthrough with an ingenious system with a double function using a "crown" (page 101, P-1842). This crown could be pulled out and turned to set the watch's hands or pressed in and turned to wind the mainspring. This dual-function mechanism outperformed all previous winding systems and was much easier to manufacture. Jean Adrien Philippe's crown-winding and setting system remains an integral part of all mechanical wristwatches. The key is gone forever (page 102, P-1592).

Philippe's invention was awarded a bronze medal at the "Exposition des produits de l'industrie française" in 1844 in Paris. When the Polish entrepreneur Antoine Norbert de Patek (1812–1877), who had already started manufacturing watches in Geneva in 1839, heard about the French watchmaker's idea, he immediately recognized its commercial potential. In 1845, Patek invited Philippe to work with him in Geneva. Both names became the trademark of the manufacturer Patek Philippe. Their partnership laid the cornerstone for a watchmaking company that would become legendary.

Coronation

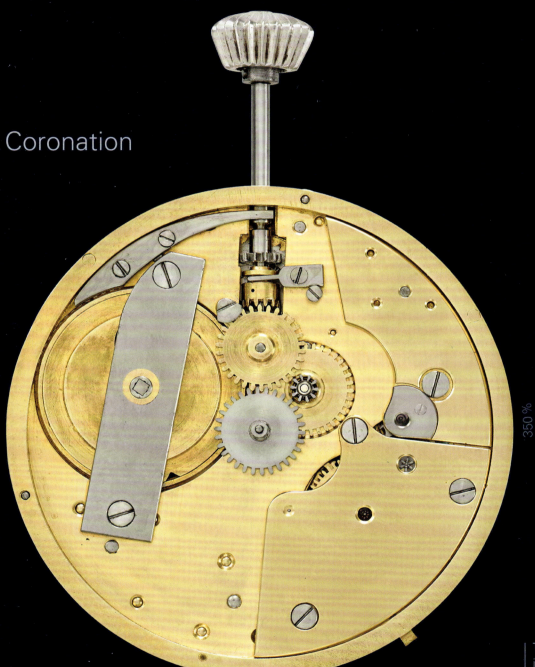

This movement is the oldest surviving example of Jean Adrien Philippe's first combined crown-winding and setting mechanism: the crown can be turned to wind the mainspring and pulled to set the hands. A key is no longer needed.

Jean Adrien Philippe
Paris, 1842
Caliber 17'''
Ø 38 mm; P-1842

Crowning of the Pocket Watch

Dual-function

This watch incorporates Jean Adrien Philippe's (1815–1894) first stem-winding and setting system. The crown could be pulled and turned to set the hands, and then pressed inward and turned to wind the mainspring. This mechanism, which used a sliding pinion, outperformed all the previous systems, and the crown has since become the standard for winding and setting watches.

Jean Adrien Philippe
Paris, circa 1845
Ø 45 mm; P-1592

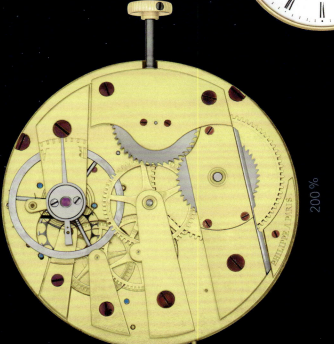

200%

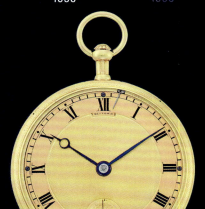

Turn the Case

German-born watchmaker Sigismund Rentzsch attempted to completely eliminate the key. This pocket watch was wound by turning its back clockwise and counter-clockwise. The hands were set by pulling out and then turning the crown in the pendant. Yet the time often still had to be set with a key.

Sigismund Rentzsch
London, circa 1815
Ø 49 mm; S-832